41 Healing Skin Cancer Meal Recipes:

The Most Complete Skin Cancer Fighting Foods to Help You heal Fast

By

Joe Correa CSN

COPYRIGHT

This publication is designed to provide accurate and authoritative information in regard to the subject matter covered. It is sold with the understanding that neither the author nor the publisher is engaged in rendering medical advice. If medical advice or assistance is needed, consult with a doctor. This book is considered a guide and should not be used in any way detrimental to your health. Consult with a physician before starting this nutritional plan to make sure it's right for you.

ACKNOWLEDGEMENTS

This book is dedicated to my friends and family that have had mild or serious illnesses so that you may find a solution and make the necessary changes in your life.

41 Healing Skin Cancer Meal Recipes:

The Most Complete Skin Cancer Fighting Foods to Help You heal Fast

By

Joe Correa CSN

CONTENTS

Copyright

Acknowledgements

About The Author

Introduction

41 Healing Skin Cancer Meal Recipes: The Most Complete Skin Cancer Fighting Foods to Help You heal Fast

Additional Titles from This Author

ABOUT THE AUTHOR

After years of Research, I honestly believe in the positive effects that proper nutrition can have over the body and mind. My knowledge and experience has helped me live healthier throughout the years and which I have shared with family and friends. The more you know about eating and drinking healthier, the sooner you will want to change your life and eating habits.

Nutrition is a key part in the process of being healthy and living longer so get started today. The first step is the most important and the most significant.

INTRODUCTION

41 Healing Skin Cancer Meal Recipes: The Most Complete Skin Cancer Fighting Foods to Help You heal Fast

By Joe Correa CSN

The most dangerous time of the year is definitely summer time, when we're exposed to the sun most of the time. A lot of people use sunscreen to protect themselves from harmful UV rays, which is a great idea. However, most of these commercial products contain toxic chemicals which block the absorption of vitamin D that we need from the sun. What can we do to protect our skin and our health? Well, just by reading this book, you took the first step in taking care of your skin and your overall health. Congratulations!

By now, you're probably wondering how a simple book can take care of your skin and prevent those nasty cancer conditions? The answer is simple, studies show that the best results in skin cancer prevention come from having a healthy diet that will help your body eliminate toxins!

The key when trying to prevent skin cancer lies in eating food rich in antioxidants, like fruits and vegetables. This book is exactly that! It has the best possible collection of carefully chosen ingredients that will help prevent skin cancer and other health conditions. Included are some powerful superfoods which are loaded with antioxidants and are perfect for boosting your immune system.

These recipes contain the most important vitamins for your skin – vitamin A, B, C, and D, and some other irreplaceable nutrients like zinc, selenium, lycopene, and essential fatty acids. These nutrients are evenly distributed between breakfast, lunch, dinner, salads, soups, and smoothies, and will cover all your daily needs.

Let's be honest, there is no "magic food" that will cure the cancer overnight! However, there are plenty of superfoods that will definitely help prevent this dangerous disease. You will find some amazing recipes like Almond Yogurt with Nuts, Veggie Omelet, and Blueberries and Peach with Almonds for breakfast.

The key point is, a healthy diet is the best choice you can make for yourself and your skin! A healthy diet goes beyond that, it even helps you recover from this terrible disease. Your body has its own natural defense mechanism and it is up to you to help make it stronger.

41 HEALING SKIN CANCER MEAL RECIPES: THE MOST COMPLETE SKIN CANCER FIGHTING FOODS TO HELP YOU HEAL FAST

Breakfast Recipes

1.   Green Cheese Omelet

Ingredients:

2 whole eggs

1 egg white

1 tbsp of olive oil

¼ oz of blue cheese (I use gorgonzola but any cheese you have on hand will work fine)

½ tsp of ground turmeric

Pinch of salt and pepper

a handful of chopped parsley, fresh

Preparation:

In a medium bowl, heat up the olive oil over medium-high heat. Meanwhile, whisk together eggs, egg white, cheese, and turmeric. Add a pinch of salt and pepper and mix well.

Pour the mixture into a frying pan. When lightly brown on one side add some chopped parsley. Wait about 15 seconds, then flip and fry for about one more minute.

Serve.

Nutrition information per serving: Calories: 71, Protein: 12g, Carbs: 2g, Fats: 8g

2. Apricot Oatmeal

Ingredients:

2 oz of oatmeal

2 oz of apricots, dried and chopped

1 oz of almonds, sliced

½ cup of Greek yogurt

½ tbsp of honey, raw

½ cup of skim milk

1 tsp of chia seeds

½ tsp of vanilla extract

½ tsp of cinnamon, ground

Preparation:

Place sliced almonds, honey and milk in a food processor. Blend for about 30 seconds. Transfer the mixture into a medium-sized bowl. Add the oatmeal, yogurt, apricots and vanilla extract, and stir well to combine. Sprinkle with cinnamon and refrigerate for 15 minutes. Serve and enjoy!

Nutritional information per serving: Calories: 129, Protein: 4.9g, Carbs: 18.9g, Fats: 4.8g

3.   Mango Muffins

Ingredients:

1 large mango, peeled, halved and pit removed

½ cup of arrowroot (or tapioca) starch

½ cup of coconut flour

2 tbsp of milk

1 tbsp of sunflower seeds

2 tsp of baking powder

¼ tsp of baking soda

1 tsp of stevia sweetener

Muffin molds

Preparation:

Preheat the oven to 350°F.

Place mango halves in the food processor. Blend for 20 seconds, then add milk and continue blending until you get a nice creamy purée.

Combine the flour, starch, baking powder, baking soda, sunflower seeds, and stevia sweetener in a large bowl and stir well. Add the purée and give it a final stir.

Spoon the mixture to the muffin molds and bake for 15 minutes, or until a toothpick inserted in the middle of a muffin comes out clean.

Nutritional information per serving: Calories: 154, Protein: 3.1g, Carbs: 35.4g, Fats: 0.9g

4. Blueberries and Peach with Almonds

Ingredients:

2 oz of blueberries

2 medium-sized peaches

1 oz of all-purpose flour

1 tsp of ground cinnamon

½ tsp of ginger, ground

1 oz of butter, melted

½ oz of almonds, chopped

2 tbsp of brown sugar

Preparation:

Preheat the oven to 350°F. In a large bowl, combine the flour, almonds, sugar, and butter. Mash with a spoon to combine the mixture. Set aside.

Place your peaches in a deep pot. Add enough water to cover and bring it to a boil. Cook for 1 minute and remove from the heat. Drain, rinse and peel. Slice each peach in half, remove the pit and chop into bite-sized pieces.

Transfer to a lightly greased baking dish. Top with the blueberries and almond mixture.

Bake for 20 minutes, or until the surface is nice and crispy. Remove from the oven and allow to cool before serving.

Nutritional information per serving: Calories: 201, Protein: 2.6g, Carbs: 24.3g, Fats: 10.1g

5.　　Veggie Omelette

Ingredients:

1 oz of broccoli

½ cup of beans of your choice

1 small carrot, sliced

1 large tomato, cut into a bite-sized pieces

1 medium-sized red onion, peeled and chopped

1 egg

1 tbsp of olive oil

¼ tsp of salt and pepper

Preparation:

Place the broccoli, carrots, tomato and beans in a deep pot. Pour enough water to cover them all and bring heat to a boil. Cook for ten minutes over medium heat. After about ten minutes, remove from the heat.

Heat up olive oil in a large frying pan over a medium-high temperature. Add onions and stir-fry until translucent. Add the broccoli vegetable mix and continue to fry for five more minutes, stirring constantly. Whisk in the egg and cook for one more minute while allowing the egg to cook flat to a semi-hard texture. Season with some salt and pepper, then serve warm and enjoy.

Nutritional information per serving: Calories: 150, Protein: 5.5g, Carbs: 11.3g, Fats: 7.9g

6.   Sweet Potato and Feta Cheese Frittata

Ingredients:

1 medium-sized sweet potato

1 red pepper, cut into bite-sized pieces

1 green pepper, cut into bite-sized pieces

2 garlic cloves, crushed

3 large eggs

1 oz Feta cheese, crumbled

¼ cup of parsley, finely chopped

¼ cup of sour cream

¼ tsp of salt and pepper

1 tbsp of olive oil

Preparation:

Wash, peel and cut the sweet potato into bite-sized pieces. Combine peppers and potato in a large bowl. Top with the finely chopped parsley, salt, and pepper. Stir well and set aside.

Preheat the oven to 350°F.

Whisk the eggs in a large bowl. Add the cheese, sour cream, and olive oil. Mix well with a fork. Pour the mixture over the potato and pepper mix and mix well.

Grease a large baking sheet with olive oil. Add the contents of the large bowl and bake for about 45 minutes. Remove from the oven and chill for at least ten minutes. Serve and enjoy!

Nutritional information per serving: Calories: 201, Protein: 10.2g, Carbs: 16.8g, Fats: 10.5g

7. Almond Milk Yogurt with Walnuts

Ingredients:

1 cup of almond milk yogurt

½ cup of walnuts, chopped

¼ cup of chia seeds

1 tbsp of fig spread

Preparation:

In a medium bowl, combine one cup of almond milk yogurt with the chia seeds. Top with chopped walnuts and fig spread, and mix. Serve promptly and enjoy!

Nutritional information per serving: Calories: 210, Protein: 3.2g, Carbs: 21.4g, Fats: 13.8g

Lunch Recipes

8.   Braised Greens with Olive Oil

Ingredients:

½ cup of brown rice

3 oz wild asparagus, finely choppd

2 oz arugula, torn

3 oz mangel leaves, torn

3 garlic cloves, crushed

¼ tsp of black pepper, ground

1 tsp of salt

¼ cup of fresh lemon juice

3 tbsp of olive oil

Preparation:

Place rice in a pot. Add 1 ½ cups of water and bring it to a boil. Cook for about 10 minutes, or until the liquid evaporates. Stir occasionally. Remove from the heat and set aside.

Fill a large pot with salted water and add the arugula, asparagus, and mangel leaves. Bring it to a boil and cook for 2-3 minutes. Remove from the heat and drain.

In a medium-sized skillet, heat up 3 tablespoons of olive oil. Add crushed garlic and stir-fry for about 3 minutes. Now add the boiled leaves, salt, pepper, and about half of the lemon juice, and stir-fry for 5 more minutes. Add rice and mix well again.

Remove from the heat. Season with more lemon juice and serve.

Nutritional information per serving: Calories: 232, Protein: 3.7g, Carbs: 25.8g, Fats: 15.7g

9.   Stuffed Grape Leaves

Ingredients:

8 oz of grape leaves

1 lb of beef, ground

2 medium-sized onions, diced

2 tbsp of olive oil

½ tsp of garlic herb seasoning

½ tsp of salt

1 tsp of fresh mint, finely chopped

¼ tsp of black pepper, ground

Preparation:

Boil four cups of water in a large, deep pot. Place the grape leaves in the pot and cook for 1 minute. Be careful not to overdo this; you just want to soften your grape leaves.

Take one large bowl and combine the ground meat with diced onions, salt, pepper and garlic herb seasoning. Mix well to combine. Place about two tablespoons of this mixture in the center of each grape leaf. Roll up nicely tuck in the ends.

Take a large saucepan and lightly grease the bottom with 1 tablespoon of olive oil. Gently place the rolls in it and add enough water to cover it. Cover with a lid and cook for about 50 minutes, over a medium-low temperature.

Serve warm and enjoy.

Nutritional information per serving: Calories: 207, Protein: 13.2g, Carbs: 18.8g, Fats: 30.2g

10.   Turkey with Broccoli

Ingredients:

8 oz of turkey breast, skinless and boneless

3 oz of broccoli, chopped

1 oz of brussel sprouts, chopped

3 garlic cloves, diced

¼ cup of fresh parsley, chopped

½ tsp of salt

¼ tsp of black pepper, ground

¼ tsp of dried oregano, minced

2 tbsp of olive oil

Preparation:

Boil the broccoli and brussel sprouts in a deep pot. Cover with a lid and add enough water to cover the vegetables. Cook for 10 minutes. Set aside with covered lid.

Heat up olive oil in frying pan over a medium-high temperature. Add the diced garlic cloves and stir-fry for about 3 minutes.

Cut the turkey meat into cubes and add to the frying pan. Continue to cook for 8 more minutes, turning over the turkey meat cubes to brown on all sides. Serve the turkey meat with the boiled broccoli mix and season with some salt, pepper, oregano, and parsley. Enjoy.

Nutritional information per serving: Calories: 163, Protein: 34.6g, Carbs: 19.6g, Fats: 27.4g

11.   Stuffed Eggplants

Ingredients:

2 medium-sized eggplants

2 small onions, peeled and finely chopped

2 cloves of garlic, crushed

¼ cup of parsley, finely chopped

1 large tomato, peeled and finely chopped

¼ tsp of salt

¼ tsp of black pepper, ground

2 tbsp of olive oil

1 bay leaf, dry and crushed

2 tbsp of almonds, finely chopped

Preparation:

Preheat the oven to 320 degrees F. Line some baking paper over a baking pan.

Slice the eggplants in half, lengthwise. Remove the flesh and place this eggplant flesh in a medium bowl for later use. Transfer the hollowed eggplants to a different bowl. Top with some salt and let it stand for about 5 minutes.

Heat up some olive oil to a medium-high temperature. Briefly fry the hollowed eggplants on each side for about 3 minutes and remove from the frying pan and set aside in a separate dish.

To the same frying pan, add the chopped onions and garlic. Stir-fry for several minutes and add the chopped tomato. Mix well and simmer until the tomatoes have softened. Now add the eggplant flesh and the salt, pepper, bay leaf, chopped almonds, and parsley to the frying pan. Cook for 5 more minutes while stirring, then remove from the heat.

Stuff the eggplant halves with this mixture. Transfer to a baking dish and bake for about 15 minutes, or until lightly charred.

Serve warm with topping of choice, such as sour cream, mustard or shredded cheese.

Nutrition information per serving: Calories: 260, Protein: 7.8g, Carbs: 45.7g, Fats: 8.9g

12.   Green Beans Goulash

Ingredients:

1 pound of beans, pre-cooked

2 medium-sized carrots, washed, sliced

1 large red bell pepper, chopped

2 medium – sized onions, sliced

5 gloves of garlic, crushed

3 tomatoes, sliced

1 cup tomato sauce

1 tbsp paprika

1 cup of celery, chopped

2 tbsp of olive oil

7 cups of water

Preparation:

In a large frying pan, heat the olive oil on high. Stir-fry the onions for 2 minutes. Add sliced carrots, pepper and garlic. Cook for about 10 minutes on high temperature. Trasnfer to a large cooking pot.

Add the tomatoes, tomato sauce, and 1 more cup of hot water. Add the pre-cooked beans and 5 cups of water. Now add the celery and paprika. Securely lock the cooking pot's lid. Cook on high for 10 minutes, then remove from heat and allow to cool. Serve and enjoy.

Nutritional information per serving: Calories: 125, Protein: 12.5g, Carbs: 18.2g, Fats: 21.3g

13.   Mixed Veggies Stir-Fry

Ingredients:

2 large red bell peppers, chopped

2 medium-sized tomatoes, chopped

½ zucchini, peeled and chopped

1 large onion, finely chopped

2 garlic gloves, crushed

3 tbsp of olive oil

¼ tsp of salt

¼ tsp of black pepper, ground

Preparation:

Thinkly slice the peppers and tomatoes, removing the seeds. Place the slices in a large bowl and mix. Set aside.

Take a large saucepan and heat up the olive oil over medium heat. Stir-fry the onion and garlic for 3 minutes and then add the chopped zucchini. Continue to cook for 5 more minutes, or until the liquid evaporates. Finally, add the tomatoes and peppers to the saucepan. Cook for

5 more minutes while stirring well. Remove from the heat and serve when slightly cooled.

Nutritional information per serving: Calories: 85, Protein: 2.3g, Carbs: 10.8g, Fats: 32.5g

14.   Veal with Leek

Ingredients:

½ lb of veal, skinless and boneless

½ lb of leek, chopped into bite-size pieces

1 large tomato, chopped

2 garlic cloves, finely chopped

3 tbsp of olive oil

½ tsp of Cayenne pepper (may use black pepper if you prefer to avoid the spicy cayenne pepper)

½ tsp of salt

Preparation:

First you need to cut the meat into bite-sized pieces. This makes the cooking process much easier and quicker. Place the chopped veal meat in a deep pot. Add enough water to cover and season with some salt. Cover and cook for about 15 minutes over medium-high heat.

Now add the chopped leek, 1 tablespoon of olive oil, and the pepper. Reduce the heat to low and continue to cook for 5 minutes.

Meanwhile, chop the onion and garlic in a food processor. About ten seconds will be enough as you don't want to purée your onions.

Heat up 2 tablespoons of olive oil in a large saucepan and add the chopped onion and garlic. Stir-fry for 3 minutes, or until translucent. Add the chopped tomato and stir-fry for 1 minute, then transfer to the veal meat pot. Cook everything together for 2 final minutes while stirring.

Remove from the heat and serve warm.

Nutritional information per serving: Calories: 205, Protein: 14.8g, Carbs: 22.4g, Fats: 28.9g

Dinner Recipes

15. Broccoli Casserole

Ingredients:

2 large broccoli crowns, chopped

1 cup brussel sprouts, halved

1 cup of quinoa, rinsed

4 cups of vegetable broth

2 small onions, finely chopped

1 cup of sour cream

2 tsp dry thyme, minced

4 tbsp of olive oil

½ tsp of salt

¼ tsp of black pepper, ground

Preparation:

Preheat the oven to 350°F.

In a large saucepan, combine quinoa with vegetable broth and dry thyme. Add some salt and pepper to taste and bring it to a boil. Reduce the heat and cook for about 12 minutes until the liquid is absorbed. Remove from the heat and set aside.

Heat up the olive oil in a large saucepan. Add onions and stir-fry for 2 minutes, or until translucent. Now add chopped broccoli and brussel sprouts. Continue to cook for about 10 more minutes, until the broccoli and brussel sprouts are tender-crisp.

In a large bowl, mix the broccoli mixture with the quinoa mixture. Add sour cream and stir well. Place in a lightly oiled shallow casserole dish. Bake for about 20 minutes, or until the top is lightly charred and crisp.

Allow to cool and serve!

Nutritional information per serving: Calories: 220, Protein: 6.4g, Carbs: 10.9g, Fats: 17.6

16.   Sweet Potato and Salmon Patties

Ingredients:

1 lb sweet potato, sliced

6 oz fresh salmon fillet

1 cup of milk

1 egg

1 tsp of sea salt

1 tbsp of butter

1 cup of all-purpose flour

½ cup of breadcrumbs

½ cup of parsley, finely chopped

1 tbsp of olive oil

Preparation:

Place the potato slices in a deep pot. Add enough water to cover and bring it to a boil. Cook until softened. Remove from the heat and transfer to a large bowl. Add the salt, milk, and butter. Mash until smooth purée then set aside.

Finely chop the salmon fillet and add to the sweet potato purée. Add the flour, eggs, and parsley, and mix well. Using your hands, shape 1-inch thick patties and coat in breadcrumbs.

Preheat some oil over a medium-high heat. Fry each patty for about 3 minutes on each side.

Serve with some fresh vegetables of your choice and enjoy.

Nutrition information per serving: Calories: 111, Protein: 8g, Carbs: 13g, Fats: 4g

17.   Grilled Shiitake Mushrooms

Ingredients:

3 oz of shiitake mushrooms

1 tsp of fresh dill

½ tsp of garlic powder

¼ tsp of salt

2 oz of fresh arugula

1 tsp of fresh rosemary, chopped

1 tsp of olive oil

½ tsp of balsamic vinegar

½ tsp of ground pepper

Preparation:

Preheat a non-stick grill pan over a medium-high temperature.

Clean, wash, and cut each mushroom in half. Place on pan and grill for 5 minutes or until the mushroom liquid evaporates, while stirring constantly. When all the liquid has evaporated, remove the mushrooms from the heat and transfer to a serving platter. Combine the olive oil with chopped rosemary, vinegar, dill, salt and pepper with the mushrooms in the serving platter and stir well. Sprinkle with some garlic powder and serve with fresh arugula.

Enjoy!

Nutrition information per serving: Calories: 119 Protein: 22g, Carbs: 1.5g, Fats: 1.7g

18.   Beans, Nuts'n Seeds

Ingredients:

1 cup of quinoa, pre-cooked

1 cup of white beans, pre-cooked

3 tbsp of hazelnuts, roasted

1 tbsp of almonds, finely chopped

1 tbsp of flaxseed

½ cup of fresh parsley

1 small onion, peeled and chopped

2 garlic cloves, finely chopped

¼ tsp of salt

5 tbsp of olive oil

1 cup of button mushrooms, sliced

Preparation:

Combine the hazelnuts, almonds, flaxseeds, parsley, salt and 3 tbsp of olive oil in a food processor. Blend well for 30 seconds.

Heat up the remaining olive oil in a large skillet. Add chopped onion and garlic. Stir-fry for several minutes, until lightly charred.

Add to the stir-fry the cooked quinoa, white beans, button mushrooms, and mix well. Cook for 5 more minutes, or until the water evaporates.

Remove from the heat and transfer to a serving bowl. Add the nut blend and mix well.

Serve and enjoy.

Nutrition information per serving: Calories: 193 Protein: 28.3g, Carbs: 40.6g, Fats: 9.9g

19.   Mozzarella Veggie Muffins

Ingredients:

2 cups of buchwheat flour

½ cup of rice flour

1 tbsp of baking powder

½ tsp of salt

1 cup of milk

2 eggs

2 tbsp of olive oil

¼ cup of Mozzarella cheese, crumbled

¼ cup of spinach, cooked and squeezed

¼ cup of broccoli, cooked and blended

Muffin molds

Preparation:

In a large bowl, combine the flours, baking powder, and salt. Gently whisk in milk and 2 eggs. Then mix well with an electric mixer. This will give you a nice, smooth muffin dough. Now add the spinach and blended broccoli and mozzarela cheese into the dough and mix well again. Shape the muffins using muffin molds.

Preheat the oven to 300 degrees F. Bake for about 25 minutes. Allow to cool and serve.

Nutrition information per serving: Calories: 176 Protein: 9.5g, Carbs: 24.2g, Fats: 8.3g

Salad Recipes

20.   Red Cabagge with Carrots Salad

Ingredients:

½ red cabbage head

2 large spring onions, washed, sliced

2 medium-sized carrots, washed, sliced

2 tbsp of olive oil

2 tbsp of fresh lemon juice

½ tsp of sea salt

½ tsp of black pepper, freshly ground

Preparation:

Cut cabbage into pieces and place it in a food processor. Pulse quickly until chopped roughly. Be careful not to process too much.

In a salad bowl, combine the cabbage with sliced carrots and spring onions. Toss with olive oil, lemon juice, sea salt, and black pepper.

Nutritional information per serving: Calories: 156, Protein: 1.1g, Carbs: 17.8g, Fats: 17.7g

21.   Beet Greens and Kale Salad

Ingredients:

2 oz of beet green leaves

2 oz of kale leaves

4 baby tomatoes

2 tbsp of olive oil

½ tsp of salt

¼ tsp black pepper, ground

1 tsp lemon juice

Preparation:

In a salad bowl, combine the beet green leaves with the kale. Toss with the baby tomatoes, olive oil, lemon juice, sea salt, and black pepper.

Serve and enjoy.

Nutritional information per serving: Calories: 158, Protein: 1.1g, Carbs: 16.5g, Fats: 8.3g

22. Radical Radish Bean Salad

Ingredients:

8 oz of precooked beans of your choice

5 radishes, sliced

1 cucumber, sliced

3 spring onions, chopped

½ cup of fresh celery, chopped

1 red pepper, sliced

1 green pepper, sliced

For the seasoning:

¼ cup of olive oil

1/8 cup of apple cider vinegar

1 tsp of chilli powder

1 tsp of fresh thyme, finely chopped

¼ tsp of salt

¼ tsp of black pepper, ground

Preparation:

Combine the seasoning ingredients in a bowl. Mix well and chill for about 15 minutes in the refrigerator.

Meanwhile, combine the precooked beans with the cucumber, green pepper, red pepper, celery, onions and radishes in a large salad bowl.

Drizzle with seasoning, serve and enjoy.

Nutritional information per serving: Calories: 359, Protein: 12.6g, Carbs: 45.8g, Fats: 20.3g

23.   Lentil Salad with Fresh Parsley

Ingredients:

1 cup of lentils

1 medium-sized spring onion, chopped

¼ cup of parsley, chopped

½ tsp of salt

¼ tsp of black pepper, freshly ground

2 tbsp of olive oil

1 tbsp of sesame seeds

Preparation:

First you have to cook your lentils. Use 3 cups of water for 1 cup of dry lentils. Cooked lentils will double in size. Keep this in mind when cooking. Bring the water to a boiling point, reduce the heat to medium and cover. Cook for about 20 minutes. Remove from the heat and drain. Allow to cool, then transfer to a salad bowl.

Now top the lentils with the onion and parsley, and season with salt, pepper, olive oil, and sprinkle with sesame seeds. Toss well and serve.

Nutritional information per serving: Calories: 300, Protein: 16.5g, Carbs: 33.6g, Fats: 12.7g

24.   Hokkaido Pumpkin with Salmon Salad

Ingredients:

½ small-sized hokkaido pumpkin, cubed

3 oz of smoked salmon, sliced

½ cup of baby spinach, finely chopped

½ cup of walnuts, chopped

1 tbsp of olive oil

1 tbsp of lemon juice

¼ tsp of salt

¼ tsp of black pepper, ground

Preparation:

First, preheat the oven to 320°F.

Now, peel the pumpkin and cut into bite-sized cubes. Line some baking paper in a baking sheet. Greese the baking sheet with olive oil. Put the pumpkin cubes in it, and add some salt and pepper. Bake for about 10 minutes, or until lightly charred.

Heat some olive oil a non-stick frying pan over a medium-high temperature. Add smoked salmon slices and grill until nice and crispy on both sides. Remove from the pan and set aside.

Spread the baby spinach over a serving plate. Top with the pumpkin cubes and smoked salmon slices. Sprinkle with walnuts and with lemon juice, olive oil, salt, and pepper. Serve promptly and enjoy!

Nutritional information per serving: Calories: 306, Protein: 13.7g, Carbs: 6.9g, Fats: 25.2g

25. Baby Spinach Salad with Fresh Apple Juice Dressing

Ingredients:

4 oz baby spinach, finely chopped

3 medium-sized spring onions, chopped

3 tbsp of apple cider vinegar

½ cup of fresh apple juice

2 tbsp of olive oil

1 tbsp of Dijon mustard

½ tsp of salt

Preparation:

In a small bowl, combine the apple juice with cider, olive oil, mustard, and salt. Mix well and set aside.

In a large salad bowl, combine the baby spinach with chopped spring onions. Top with the apple dressing and mix well. Serve and enjoy.

Nutrition information per serving: Calories: 107, Protein: 5.9g, Carbs: 11.4g, Fats: 5.3g

Soup Recipes

26.   Mashed Beans Soup

Ingredients:

1 cup of beans of your choice, cooked and drained

1 small carrot

1 small onion

¼ tsp of salt

¼ tsp of freshly ground black pepper

1 tbsp of olive oil

Preparation:

Wash the onions and carrots, but do not chop them. Put them together with the beans in a boiling pan. Add salted water and cook for 5 minutes. Remove from the heat and allow to cool for 5 minutes. Place the boiled onions, carrots and beans in a blender, but leave the water remainder in the pan. Blend until smooth.

Heat up the remaining vegetable water to a boiling point and stir with a little oil. Cook until the mixture thickens, add the blended vegetables and cook for another 5 minutes.

Serve warm.

Nutrition information per serving: Calories: 95, Protein: 5.9g, Carbs: 11.8g, Fats: 5g

27. Caliuflower Soup

Ingredients:

1 large cauliflower head, cut into bite-sized pieces

1 cup of cottage cheese, crumbled

2 tbsp olive oil

1 garlic clove, crushed

1 leek, chopped

1 tbsp of butter

4 oz vegetable stock

½ tsp of salt

Preparation:

Place caliuflower and cottage cheese into a food processor. Blend for 30 seconds and set aside.

Heat the olive oil in a large pot over a medium-high temperature. Add butter, garlic and leek and cook for 3 minutes.

Transfer the cauliflower and cheese mixture to the pot and add the vegetable broth. Cover, reduce the heat to low and cook for 25 minutes.

Serve warm.

Nutritional information per serving: Calories: 132, Protein: 9.3g, Carbs: 21.4g, Fats: 7.9g

28.   Carrot Soup

Ingredients:

5 large carrots, washed, sliced

1 cup of vegetable broth

2 cups of water

¼ tsp of sea salt

¼ tsp of ground pepper

1 tsp of dry rosemary

Preparation:

Heat a large cooking pot with the 2 cups of water to a medium-high temperature. Place all the ingredients in a deep cooking pot. Cook for 5 minutes while stirring. Cover with lid and cook for 5 additional minutes. Turn off heat, remove lid and stir gently for 2 minutes.

Serve warm and enjoy.

Nutritional information per serving: Calories: 96, Protein: 6.3g, Carbs: 14.6g, Fats: 4.2g

29.   Green Beans and Broccoli Soup

Ingredients:

8 oz of green beans

1 small onion, sliced

2 cups of broccoli, finely chopped

1 garlic clove, whole

¼ tsp of ground pepper

¼ tsp of salt

2 tbsp olive oil

1 bay leaf

¼ cup of sour cream

Preparation:

Soak the beans overnight. Rinse and drain.

Place the beans, olive oil, broccoli, garlic, and onion into blender with ½ cup of water. Blend for 2 minutes until smooth.

Now, place all ingredients into a deep pot and cook for about 30 minutes while stirring ocassionally.

When serving, top soup with a dab of sour cream.

Serve warm and enjoy.

Nutritional information per serving: Calories: 115, Protein: 4.3g, Carbs: 15.7g, Fats: 4.6g

30. Creamy Button Mushroom Coconut and Carrot Soup

Ingredients:

1 carrot, diced

½ cup of shredded coconut

1 cup of coconut milk

1 cup of button mushrooms, thinly sliced

5 cups of water

1 tsp of pepper

1 celery, chopped

1 tbsp of olive oil

1 tsp of sea salt

1 green pepper, chopped, seed removed

3 onions, chopped

Preparation:

Heat the olive oil in a deep pot on medium-high temperature. Add the onions, carrots, and shredded coconut. Cook for about 5 minutes and then add the mushrooms, celery and pepper and continue cooking while stirring for 5 more minutes.

Pour the coconut milk and water. Reduce the heat, cover and cook for 20 minutes.

Remove from the heat, season with salt and pepper, serve and enjoy.

Nutrition information per serving: Calories: 130, Protein: 2.3g, Carbs: 9.2g, Fats: 14.4g

31. Tomato Soup

Ingredients:

8 tomatoes, peeled and roughly chopped

½ cup of celery, finely chopped

1 medium-sized onion, diced

¼ cup of fresh basil, finely chopped

½ tsp of black pepper, ground

4 cups of water

1 tbsp olive oil

Preparation:

Preheat the non-stick frying pan with the olive oil over a medium-high temperature. Add the onions, celery, and fresh basil. Sprinkle with some pepper and stir-fry for about 10 minutes, until caramelized.

To a large cooking pan, add the tomatoes and about 1 cup of water. Place the heat to medium-low and cook for about 15 minutes, until softened. Now add about 1 cup of water and bring it to a boil. Add the onion, celery, basil mixture to the boil and cook for 2 minutes while stirring. Remove from the heat and serve with fresh parsley.

Nutrition information per serving: Calories: 25, Protein: 0.7g, Carbs: 8.9g, Fats: 0.9g

32.   Brussel Sprouts Soup

Ingredients:

2 cups fresh brussel sprouts, halved

¼ cup of fresh parsley, finely chopped

1 tsp of dry thyme

1 tbsp of fresh lemon juice

¼ tsp of sea salt

Preparation:

Place the brussel sprouts in a deep pot and pour enough water to cover the sprouts. Bring it to a boil and cook until tender. Remove from the heat and drain.

Transfer the tendered sprouts to a food processor. Add fresh parsley, thyme, and about ½ cup of water. Pulse until smooth mixture. Return to a boiling pot and add 1 cup of water. Bring it to a boil and cook for 10 minutes, over a low temperature. Season with salt, serve warm and enjoy.

Nutritional information per serving: Calories: 87, Protein: 3.5g, Carbs: 7.6g, Fats: 5.3g

33.   Chicken Soup with Garlic

Ingredients:

2 chicken breast, boneless and skinless

1 tbsp of parsley, freshly grounded

5 garlic cloves, finely chopped

1 small onion, chopped

1 tbsp of all-purpose flour

4 tbsp of olive oil

½ tsp of salt

¼ tsp of black pepper, ground

Preparation:

Preheat 2 tablespoons of olive oil in a frying skillet over a medium-high temperature. Add onion and 3 garlic cloves. Stir-fry until translucent.

Transfer onion and garlic into a deep cooking pot. Add chicken breasts, parsley, salt and pepper. Pour enough water to cover all ingredients. Cover and cook for 30 minutes on low heat.

Drain the soup into a large bowl. Chop the cooked chicken into bite-size pieces.

Heat up 2 tablespoons of olive oil in a deep cooking pot over a medium-high temperature. Transfer the bite-size chicken pieces into the pot with the finely chopped garlic and cook for 1 minute. Add the flour and continue cooking while stirring for 2 more minutes.

Finally, pour the drained soup into the chicken pot and give it a gentle stir while cooking for 10 minutes. Serve warm and enjoy.

Nutritional information per serving: Calories: 93, Protein: 12.8g, Carbs: 16.5g, Fats: 22.4g

34. Carrot and Beef Soup

Ingredients:

8 oz of beef, skinless and boneless

3 medium-sized carrots, washed, chopped

1 medium-sized onion, chopped

1 large egg

1 tsp of sour cream

2 tsp of parlsey, finely chopped

2 bay leaves

4 tbsp of olive oil

½ tsp of salt

½ tsp of black pepper, ground

Preparation:

First, place the meat in a deep cooking pot. Pour enough water to cover the meat. Cover, reduce the heat to low temperature and cook for 30 minutes until soft.

Meanwhile, heat up some olive oil in a frying pan over medium-high temperature. Add chopped onions and carrots. Pour 1 cup of water and cook until softened.

Transfer the fried vegetables to the cooking pot. Add water to cover the ingredients. Cook for 30 minutes.

Add the salt, pepper and bay leaves and reduce the temperature to low.

Meanwhile, whisk the egg together with the sour cream. Place it in the pot and stir gently for 1 minute. Finally, add the fresh finely chopped parsley, and leave the cooking pot on medium-low for 2 minutes.

Serve warm and enjoy.

Nutritional information per serving: Calories: 110, Protein: 8.7g, Carbs: 9.4g, Fats: 18.5g

35.   Eggplant Soup

Ingredients:

3 small eggplants, peeled and cut into bite-sized pieces

1 medium-sized red onion, finely chopped

2 medium sized tomatoes, peeled and chopped

1 tbsp of sour cream

2 tbsp of olive oil

½ tsp of salt

½ tsp of black pepper, ground

¼ tsp of chili pepper, ground

Preparation:

Put eggplant cubes in a large bowl, and add the salt. Set aside for about 15 minutes (salt will take out most of the eggplant bitterness).

Heat up the 2 tablespoons of olive oil in a large frying pan over medium-high temperature. Add finely chopped onion and stir fry until translucent. Add eggplant cubes and stir fry for 2 minutes. Now, take out 2 tablespoons of eggplant cubes and set aside in a small bowl.

Add chopped tomatoes to the frying pan and stir well. Cook for 3 minutes more and leave it to cool of a while. Transfer everything from the frying pan to a food processor and blend until smooth.

Take a large deep pot and transfer the mixture from the food processor. Add 1 cup of water, salt, black pepper, and chili pepper, and cover with a lid. Cook for 15 minutes.

Serve with the remaining fried eggplant bite-sized cubes, and enjoy.

Nutritional information per serving: Calories: 125, Protein: 5.6g, Carbs: 17.4g, Fats: 19.7g

Smoothie Recipes

36.   Orange and Banana Smoothie

Ingredients:

2 large oranges, peeled and halved

1 banana, peeled and roughly chopped

1 tsp of lemon juice

1 tsp of honey, raw

¼ tsp of cinammon, ground

Preparation:

Combine the banana, oranges, lemon juice and honey in a food processor and blend. Pour it in a cup and add cinammon on top. Mix witha spoon.

Serve with ice and enjoy.

Nutritional information per serving: Calories: 137, Protein: 2.0g, Carbs: 35.3g, Fats: 0.5g

37.   Green Veggies Smoothie

Ingredients:

¼ cup of broccoli, cut in half

¼ cup of brussel sprouts, cut in half

¼ cup of spinach, finely chopped

1 tsp of lemon juice

1 cup of orange juice

¼ tsp of ground mint

Preparation:

Cook the broccoli, brussel sprouts, and spinash in a pot of boiling water for 10 minutes, until softened. Drain well cooking and allow to cool for 5 minutes.

Transfer the veggies into a food processor. Add the ground mint, lemon juice and orange juice and blend until smooth. Refrigerate for 15 minutes.

Add some ice cubes when serving and enjoy!

Nutritional informations per serving: Calories: 73, Protein: 6.3g, Carbs: 14.1g, Fats: 0.4g

38.   Carrot Ginger Smoothie

Ingredients:

4 large carrots, washed, sliced

1 orange, cut in wedges

¼ cup of ginger root, sliced

1 cup of fresh apple juice

Preparation:

Combine the ingredients in a food processor and pulse until smooth. Serve cold and enjoy!

Nutritional informations per serving: Calories: 97, Protein: 4.2g, Carbs: 14.1g, Fats: 0.4g

39. Fresh Apple and Fig Smoothie

Ingredients:

1 small green apple, sliced

4 fresh figs, halved

1 kiwi, peeled and sliced

¼ cup of finely chopped spinach

Juice from 1 lime

½ tsp of stevia sweetener

½ cup of milk

½ cup of water

Preparation:

Combine all ingredients in a blender. Blend on high until smooth. Serve cold and enjoy.

Nutritional information per serving: Calories: 243, Protein: 4.7g, Carbs: 26.8g, Fats: 5.5g

40.   Kale Smoothie with Almond Milk

Ingredients:

1 cup of almond milk

1 cup of raw kale, finely chopped

½ peach, sliced

1 slice of melon

1 tsp of ground turmeric

1 tbsp of sesame seeds

1 tsp of stevia sweetener

Preparation:

Place the ingredients in a food processor. Turn on until smooth. Serve cold and enjoy.

Nutritional information per serving: Calories: 153, Protein: 4.8g, Carbs: 45.5g, Fats: 4.3g

41. Coconut Detox Smoothie

Ingredients:

1cup of coconut water

¼ cup of baby spinach, finely chopped

½ cup of green tea

¼ cup of cucumber, peeled and chopped

½ avocado, chopped

1 tsp vanilla extract

2 tsp stevia sweetener

Preparation:

Combine the ingredients in a blender and blend for about 40 seconds. Chill well, serve and enjoy.

Nutritional information per serving: 110, Protein: 4.2g, Carbs: 8.5g, Fats: 3.4g

ADDITIONAL TITLES FROM THIS AUTHOR

70 Effective Meal Recipes to Prevent and Solve Being Overweight: Burn Fat Fast by Using Proper Dieting and Smart Nutrition

By

Joe Correa CSN

48 Acne Solving Meal Recipes: The Fast and Natural Path to Fixing Your Acne Problems in Less Than 10 Days!

By

Joe Correa CSN

41 Alzheimer's Preventing Meal Recipes: Reduce or Eliminate Your Alzheimer's Condition in 30 Days or Less!

By

Joe Correa CSN

70 Effective Breast Cancer Meal Recipes: Prevent and Fight Breast Cancer with Smart Nutrition and Powerful Foods

By

Joe Correa CSN

CPSIA information can be obtained
at www.ICGtesting.com
Printed in the USA
BVHW052203050423
661850BV00013B/407